# EATING
## LIKE THE
# PROPHET

WRITTEN BY MOIN UDDIN KHAN
ILLUSTRATED BY KAMRUL HUSSAIN

# Eating
## Like The
# PROPHET

Published by IDEA Press
Copyright © IDEA Press 2014
ISBN 978-0-9929736-0-5
A Project of SHADE

**Proceeds generated from the sales of these publications will go towards SHADE which is a UK registered charity.**

To purchase 'Just Like The Prophet' series and other publications please contact:

w: ideauk.org
e: info@ideauk.org
t: +44 (0) 20 7998 7768

# Author's Note

All praise to Allah Lord of the worlds and salutations upon His Messenger Muhammad ﷺ.

This book teaches the Sunnah practices of the Prophet Muhammad ﷺ in terms of eating, it mentions over 40 etiquette in sequence and in simple rhyming English.

This endeavour was to provide an alternative to the common nursery rhymes and to help develop an Islamic identity. Every line has at least one Sunnah backed by a verse of the Holy Qur'an or Hadith. Even though it's aimed towards children, adults can also benefit by the rhyming easy to remember lines.

An immense amount of effort has been made to bring this project to this stage. We would like to thank all those who have supported with time, effort and funds.

Whatever is correct of this work is from Allah and His Messenger.ﷺ Whatever mistakes therein is from myself and Shaytan.

Moin Uddin Khan
*(a humble servant in need of Allah)*
London, UK
Shaban 1435 / June 2014

*Dedicated to my dear mother*
*Who sacrificed her wishes*
*to ensure our upbringing*

Allah All-Mighty made humans in perfect form,
He made Muhammad ﷺ the best to be born,
from his life there are inspirations to be drawn,
we should follow him in the way he has shown.

He would accept invitations,
even from the poor.

He would seek permission,
before entering the door.

He would greet the host,
and would sit on the floor.

He would eat what's on offer,
without asking for more.

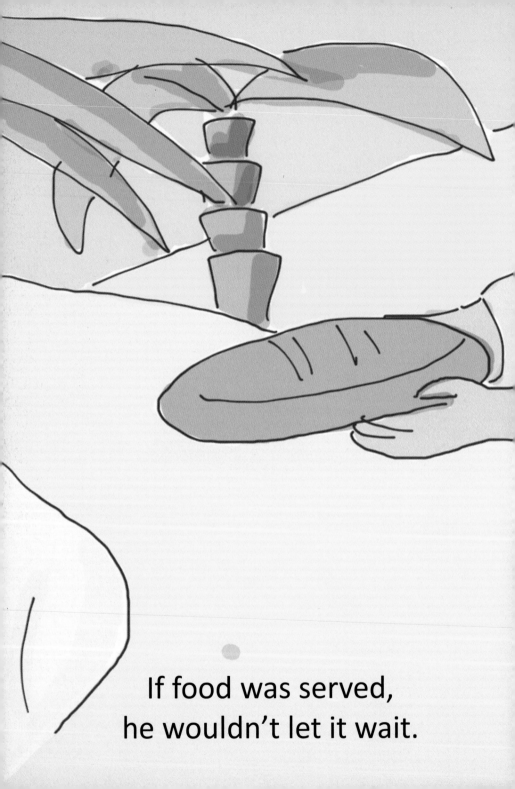

If food was served,
he wouldn't let it wait.

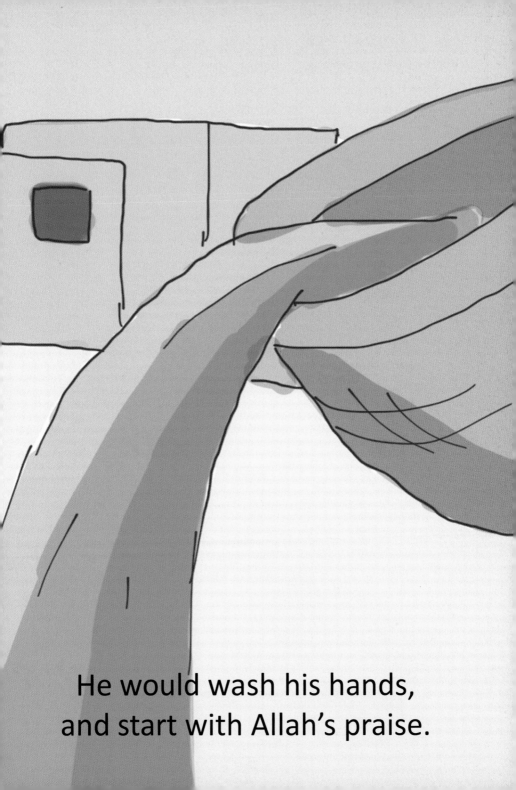

He would wash his hands,
and start with Allah's praise.

He would use his right hand,
and take what's close on his plate.

If the food was hot,
he would let it cool and not haste.

Some of his favourite food,
were milk, cucumber and dates.

If the food was good,
he would compliment the taste.

If it wasn't good, he would leave it without complaint.

He would eat from the sides,
as in the middle blessing is placed.

He wouldn't lean,
but he would sit up straight.

When eating with others,
he would try to make space.

He would pick up the morsels,
that may have escaped.

He would lick his blessed fingers,
and would clean the plate.

He would read "All praise to Allah who gave us food that we ate, who gave us drink and has made us from the people of faith".

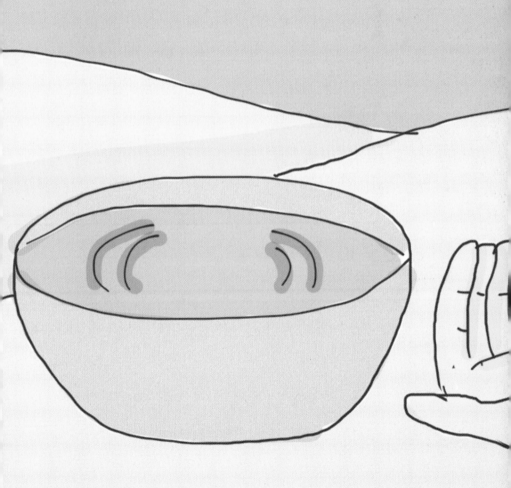

He would drink up to one third
water, and would sip in threes.

He would use a cup, but not the
side with a chipped piece.

He wouldn't fill his stomach,
he would leave space to breathe.

He would advise seeking cure, in honey and black seed.

He would wash his hands clean,
and to Allah he would plead.

"Oh Allah,
please feed the one
who has fed me".

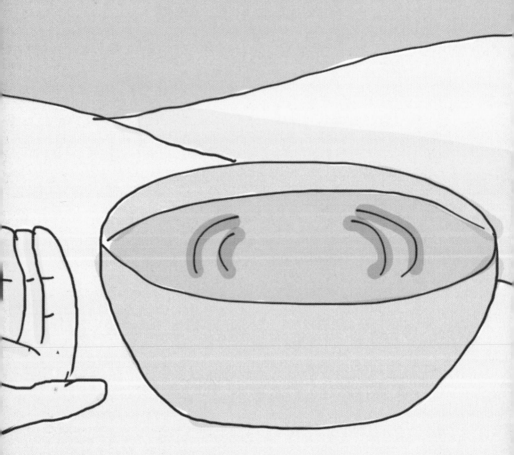

When he received food,
he would send it to others in need.

He would ensure that his neighbours had enough to eat.

He would go for weeks,
on only water and dates.

On days of hunger,
he would tie stones to his waist.

A day in the life of the
Most Praised.

We ask Allah that He helps us
to act in this way.
Amin.

'This book is the first publication of the
'Just Like The Prophet Series'

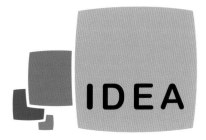

Islamic Dissemination & Education Academy

More titles coming soon InshaAllah

# About SHADE

SHADE is a UK based charitable umbrella organisation, which endeavours to help society tackle many of the challenges it faces. SHADE runs various projects and activities for the community at large, its programmes engage people from all walks of life and brings them together to encourage respect, understanding and tolerance. It has five different sectors in which there are projects dealing with different aspects of an individual's needs. This has been divided into five sectors: Social, Health, Education, Spiritual and Humanitarian.

# Support Us

## Text: IDEA33 £10 to 70070

## Visit: www.theshade.org/donate

## Phone: 020 7998 7768

## Bank Transfer: HSBC Bank a/c: 12030748 s/c: 40-02-34

**UK Charity No. 1149699**

The Shade Centre
Unit 1, Church Rd Studios
62 Church Road, London E12 6AF
W: www.theshade.org | E: info@theshade.org